THE PLAY OF DANIEL

DANIEL AS A SCRIBE

A THIRTEENTH-CENTURY MUSICAL DRAMA

The Play of Daniel

EDITED FOR MODERN PERFORMANCE

BY NOAH GREENBERG

Based on the transcription from

BRITISH MUSEUM EGERTON 2615
by REV. REMBERT WEAKLAND, O.S.B.

Narration by W. H. AUDEN

NEW YORK • OXFORD UNIVERSITY PRESS • MCMLIX

Preface

BY E. MARTIN BROWNE

The Play of Daniel is a fully developed example of an art form which is almost unknown to the modern world—liturgical drama. To perform it and to appreciate it, one needs to realize the nature of the collaboration between the creative artists and the Christian Church from which this drama grew.

When Charlemagne was crowned Emperor in A.D. 800, a stability was afforded to Christendom sufficient to allow of a great revival in the Church and a great resurgence of all the creative arts. The former led, among other things, to the codification of the Gregorian chant, the musical setting of the church services. This Introit or that Antiphon was henceforth to be sung only to the melody prescribed for it. At the same time, the artistic rebirth released a flood of musical talent. This talent could not express itself within the liturgy—because the chant was already laid down—unless it could find a way of adding its own creation to the officially chosen music.

A violinist may improvise a cadenza which adds the outpouring of his own spirit to the composition of an older master. The composers of the ninth and tenth centuries embellished the chant by adding to it or enclosing it in their own creations, which were given the name of "tropes." Especially at the great Festivals, they expressed the writer's overflowing joy both in the glory of God—as revealed by the birth and the Resurrection of Christ—and in the practice of his own art of music.

Words were soon set to the tropes, perhaps to make the elaborate melodies easier to remember, but also to add to their expressiveness. Some of the words were in the form of dialogue; and soon we find the germ of drama:

INTERROGATIO:
Quem quaeritis in sepulchro, Christicolae?
RESPONSIO:
Jesum Nazarenum crucifixum, o caelicolae.

Non est hic, surrexit sicut praedixerat;
ite, nuntiate quia surrexit de sepulchro.

The interrogators, seated at the tomb of Christ, are two deacons. "Whom seek ye in the sepulchre, O followers of Christ?" they ask. The response is given by the three who advance up the chancel with their heads covered and bearing thuribles filled with incense "as though seeking something." They are the Marys bringing their spices: "We seek Jesus of Nazareth who was crucified, O celestial ones." The two angels reply: "He is not here, he is risen as he foretold; go, announce that he is risen from the tomb." And the three make their announcement in the words of the antiphon, which leads into the liturgical service.

This incipient drama is soon given freedom to develop by being detached from the Mass and transferred to other offices, for instance to the end of Matins. The Easter music-drama expands from its four-line original into a complex of many scenes. At Christmas, drama grows from a dialogue with the shepherds at the manger, *Quem quaeritis, pastores*—obviously an imitation of the Easter trope. Around this appear plays on related subjects, suggested by the readings provided for the offices of Christmastide. One of the offices contains a sermon setting forth the series of prophecies in the Old Testament which foretell the coming of the Christ. Here is material for a dramatic Procession of Prophets; and prominent in this play is Daniel, whose canonical book is read in the office during the month of November.

It is not surprising to find that full-scale plays are soon made out of the life-story of the great announcer of the Messiah. The wandering scholar Hilarius, a pupil of Abelard, introduces into his version an incident from the apocryphal book of Bel and the Dragon (when the angel brings Habakkuk by the hair of his head to give Daniel food in the prison) and develops the character of the Queen. Our play of Daniel from Beauvais takes over and improves upon much that Hilarius has done, making a still finer drama—or, since it is entirely set to music, should we leap over five centuries and say "opera"? It is only in the angel's final passage that we can perceive traces of liturgical music, but the suggestion that the play has its roots in the liturgy is confirmed by the *Te Deum* which ends it and presumably indicates that it remains part of the church worship. For the rest, this fully grown work of art draws on the rhythms and melodies of the *trouvères* who journeyed over France delighting its people with song and story, and from the art of those folk themselves. It is one of the chefs-d'oeuvre of that second medieval renascence which took place in the twelfth century.

We can see a number of reasons why plays of this type became one of the major features of that renascence. From the point of view of the clergy, drama provided an excellent medium of instruction. The layman, who did not understand the Latin in which the liturgy was written and so could not learn from it the content of the scriptures, had their stories brought to stirring life for him in the plays. Though they too were at this time in Latin, the authors occasionally introduced vernacular phrases: and the French spectator may well have been comforted by such a mixture of tongues as the Princes' address to Daniel:

Vir propheta Dei, Daniel,
　　Vien al Roi.
　Veni, desiderat
　　Parler a toi

The barrier of language, however, must have been broken through mainly by the visual and emotional impact of the acting—which introduced a new experience into church-going—and by the power of the music.

To these elements is added another of great popular appeal—the spectacular. Within a playing-time of barely an hour we have a dozen processions, some of them accompanied by great pomp. Remembering that the play was created at the period when the magnificent series of cathedrals and great churches which enrich the European scene were just built or in building, we realize that the authors of such plays as *Daniel* were skillfully exploiting the opportunity offered by the great architectural spaces for pageantry and display. Remembering too that the Crusades were at that moment bringing Occident and Orient into close contact with each other, we may surmise that the Persian elements in the Daniel story made it especially attractive.

We saw earlier that the composers of the period needed musical scope beyond that afforded by the codified chant. This is true also in terms of emotion. The liturgy is by its nature somewhat impersonal and objective. The plays allowed free rein to emotion and to lyricism, such as may be found for instance in Daniel's lament. Yet this greater range of feeling is fitted into the framework of the service, and so the spontaneous freshness of its expression is contained within the balance and harmony of the Christian view of the world.

The Play of Daniel was created, so the prologue tells us, by "the youth" of Beauvais. A company of young singer-actors and instrumentalists can re-create it today if they will use the care and the imagination necessary to carry themselves back into the idiom and the spirit of its originators. Of the idiom, musical and dramatic, let those speak who gained experience in making the beautiful production staged by Pro Musica in New York. Of the spirit, let me conclude by saying this: for medieval man, every form of art contained a double joy—the joy of what it is in itself and the joy of what it symbolizes. The order of nature is a reflection of the Creator's love; the order of human society can at its best prefigure that of the City of God. So it is the highest joy to set forth, by means of one's own creative gifts, the pattern of heaven on earth. This is what gives to such a work as *Daniel* its combination of a robust strength and a realistic clarity with a radiant faith.

Contents

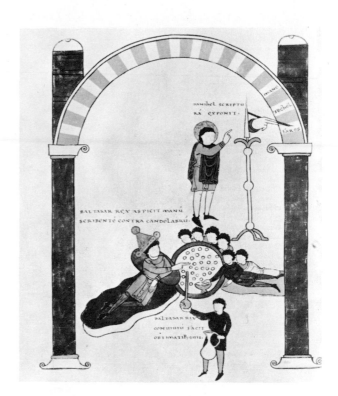

DANIEL READS THE WRITING ON THE WALL

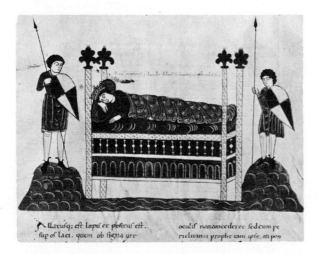

DARIUS IN TROUBLED SLEEP

Acknowledgments

We are indebted to the Trustees of the British Museum for making available Egerton MS 2615, which includes the Beauvais Daniel play, and the Bibliothèque Nationale, Paris, for allowing us to reprint photographs of the medieval illustrations. We are equally grateful to Margaret B. Freeman, curator of The Cloisters, and Professor Meyer Shapiro of Columbia University for their helpful advice during the preparation of The Cloisters production.

The music of *The Play of Daniel* has been recorded by the New York Pro Musica and is available on the following labels:

United States and Canada: Decca DL 9402 (Stereo DL 79402)

Continental Europe: Deutsche Grammophon Gesellschaft

Great Britain: Brunswick

Editor's Introduction

During January, 1958, the New York Pro Musica presented *The Play of Daniel* at the Cloisters of the Metropolitan Museum of Art. This was the first public performance since medieval times, and those of us involved in the preparation felt we had the responsibility to present both an historically "accurate" version as well as living performances that would do justice to this truly remarkable piece.

The present practical edition of the Beauvais *Play of Daniel** is based on the transcription by the Reverend Rembert Weakland, O.S.B. Father Weakland worked from the unique source, British Museum Egerton MS 2615, and his tasks were to transcribe the music into modern notation and to work out a rhythmic realization based on thirteenth-century practice.

The problems confronting the editor and performer of a work like *The Play of Daniel* are numerous. While we do have a complete musical setting with stage instructions, the MS does not indicate rhythm, instrumentation, tempi, or dynamics. There can be little doubt that the work was intended for soloists and choir, as the stage directions are quite specific in this regard. For example, the rubric preceding Belshazzar's feast reads: *The Satraps sing this song of praise to the King as they bring the vessels*, and this certainly indicates that "Jubilemus" is to be sung by a choir. That Belshazzar's part was intended for a soloist

is shown by the direction following the appearance of the handwriting on the wall (p. 26): . . . *the King upon seeing it, is frightened and exclaims* . . . There is even one indication for responsorial singing (solo and chorus) during the processional of the captive Daniel before Belshazzar. The ancient practice of antiphonal singing (alternating choirs) is not suggested in the MS but was surely used in performances of the play during the Middle Ages.

The rubrics mention instruments once: *Suddenly King Darius appears with his Princes, and before him come the kithara players* . . . However, there are further references to instruments in the Latin verse. During the Darius processional the soldiers sing: "Let the drums sound forth, let the harp players pluck their strings, let the instruments of the musicians resound in his praise." While the Queen enters the court her procession sings, " . . . with sonorous tones of strings and voices let music now be made." Thus on the basis of purely internal evidence—leaving aside our present knowledge of medieval performance practice—one can conclude that the Beauvais performances included the wide variety of instruments in use at the time. Although tempo and dynamic indications were not used, it would be hard to imagine Daniel's interpretation and Belshazzar's feast sung on the same dynamic level. It would be equally difficult to hear the deliberate Darius march into Belshazzar's court in the same tempo as Daniel's joyous processional before Darius.

At The Cloisters the singers of the New York Pro Musica played and sang the leading roles; a

---

*The reader is referred to the excellent historical articles on Liturgical Drama by D. W. L. Smolden in the *New Oxford History of Music*, Vol. II, and the Fifth Edition of *Grove's Dictionary*.

boys' choir of eight sopranos played the satraps and soldiers, and four baritones sang the parts of the wise men, the legates, and men of the court (referred to as "Princes" in the MS). The role of Belshazzar's Prince was created so that responsorial singing could be used in some of the processions.

In our edition, as in the performance, no polyphony or harmony is added, but doubling at the unison and the octave is used extensively. Since drone instruments such as the bagpipes and hurdy-gurdy were common in the Middle Ages, we add a drone bass to the sections where it seems plausible and appropriate. The melody instruments double the voices or play heterophonically, and the percussion is scored so that the different characters are identified with certain sounds; i.e. the Queen with finger cymbals, Darius with small cymbals, the envious counselors with sleigh bells, etc. We use a thirteenth-century instrumental dance as an introduction and fanfares played by a herald's trumpet before the Kings are addressed.

The size of the choir may vary and this will depend on available forces. The musical director will have to train his singers so that they have the text and music memorized. He must also arrange to have one of the instrumentalists give pitches to the singers at the beginning of each new section.

In preparing this practical performing edition we have found it necessary to transpose sections for reasons of range and tessitura. The accidentals in [square brackets] are Father Weakland's editorial suggestions. Since instruments like the psaltery and rebec are not readily available, we have substituted the modern instruments that come closest in sound. Listed below are the instruments used in the Cloisters performance and their equivalents used in the present edition:

straight trumpet	*trumpet in C*
rebec	*oboe*
recorders (soprano and sopranino)	*soprano recorder*
bowed vielle	*viola*
bell carillon	*bell carillon or chimes*
hand bells	*hand bells*
psaltery	*zither or auto harp (without dampers)*
portative organ	*soprano recorder (or modern organ)*
minstrel's harp	*guitar*

There is no question but that instruments add a great deal of color to a performance of *The Play of Daniel*, but it is perfectly possible to give it without any of the instruments listed above. A modern organ can supply the drones for the pieces that require them, and can perhaps play the trumpet fanfares as well. It would be more difficult to do without the percussion which are played by various members of the cast.

Noah Greenberg

New York
August 1959

THE PLAY OF DANIEL

The Play of Daniel

CHARACTERS

SOLO VOICES

BELSHAZZAR'S PRINCE	*Tenor*
BELSHAZZAR	*Bass*
TWO WISE MEN	*Baritones*
BELSHAZZAR'S QUEEN	*Soprano*
DANIEL	*Tenor*
DARIUS	*Baritone*
TWO ADVISERS	*Baritones*
FIRST LEGATE	*Bass*
FIRST ENVIOUS COUNSELOR	*Tenor or Soprano*
SECOND ENVIOUS COUNSELOR	*Soprano or Tenor*
FIRST ANGEL	*Soprano*
HABAKKUK	*Baritone*
SECOND ANGEL	*Tenor*

CHOIR*

SATRAPS AND QUEEN'S ATTENDANTS	*Eight Sopranos*
SOLDIERS, WISE MEN, LEGATES, ADVISERS, AND MEN OF THE COURT	*Four Tenors* *Four Baritones* *Four Basses*

*The size of the choir may vary.

INSTRUMENTALISTS

HERALD	*Trumpet in C*
FIRST MUSICIAN	*Soprano recorder*
SECOND MUSICIAN	*Oboe*
THIRD MUSICIAN	*Bell carillon or small chimes* *Handbells in E, A, G, C*
FOURTH MUSICIAN	*Viola*
ATTENDANT TO DANIEL	*Zither or autoharp (with dampers removed)*
ATTENDANT TO QUEEN (later with first angel)*	*Guitar*

PERCUSSION
(played by various members of the court)

Small drum (or bongo drum)
Large drum (tenor or bass)
Small triangle
Tambourine
Finger cymbals (oriental)
Small cymbals (7"–8" diameter)
Sleighbells, mounted on handle
Wood block

ACTORS

FIRST MONK (*Narrator*)
SECOND MONK (*for handwriting on the wall*)
TWO LIONS

A THIRTEENTH~CENTURY MUSICAL DRAMA

Trumpet-player enters in darkness. At the first trumpet call, lights on. With the second trumpet call the Narrator enters from side entrance, slowly ascends the pulpit and starts the first narration as the trumpet-player moves to the opposite side of the stage.

NARRATOR:

Welcome, good people, watch and listen
To a play in praise of the prophet Daniel,
Beloved of the Lord. Long has he dwelt
In brick Babylon, built by a river,
Far from Jerusalem, his real home,
A son of Judah, suffering exile
Since Jehoakim turned from the true God
To worship idols in high places.
Painful was the price to be paid for that:
For the cruel king of the Chaldees,
Nebuchadnezzar with a numberless host
Besieged Jerusalem and soon prevailed.
He broke her gates, burned her with fire,
Her men and women he made captive,
Her temple treasures he took away,

Shut them in the house of Shinah, his ungod,
A brass thing in which no breath was.
But Daniel, the pious, from the days of his youth,
Worshipped the One and walked humbly,
So God gave him gifts of vision
That found him favor in this foreign land.
He alone was ready to read the dreams
That Nebuchadnezzar in the night had,
And the fate he foretold befell that king,
Whole senses forsook him for seven years;
Like a witless ox he ate grass,
Nameless, naked, his nails like claws.
Those days are done. He died, and now
His son Belshazzar sits on the throne.
See, he approaches, his princes with him.

The instruments enter from the far entrance. The procession comes down the main aisle to the acting area and should be arranged on opposite sides of the throne.

[9]

[11]

Rec.	
Oboe	
Viola	
H. Bells	
Tamb.	
'm. Cym.	

Moderately slow
mf

Belshazzar's Prince

Ad ho- no- rem_ tu- i,_ Chri- ste,

Da- ni- e- lis_ lu- dus i- ste,

In Bel- va- co_ est in- ven- tus,

Et_ in- ve- nit hunc_ ju- ven- tus.

attacca

During the following the boys enter first, the men second, and the King third. He crosses to the throne. All bow as they sing: "Rex, in eternum vive!" The narration begins before the music fades away.

As King Belshazzar approaches, his princes sing this song before him:

[13]

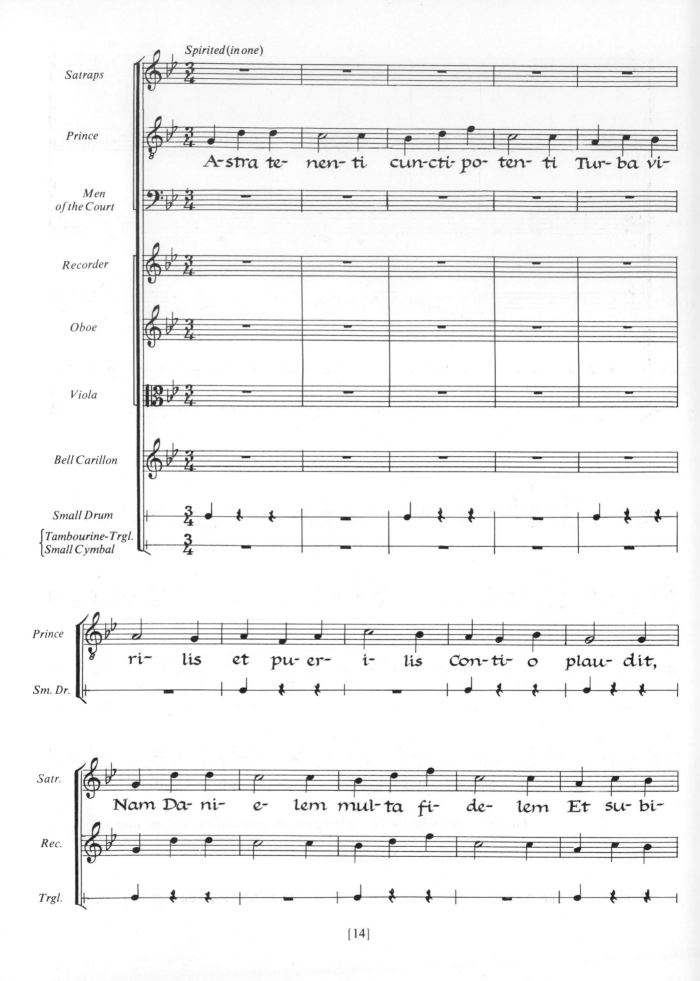

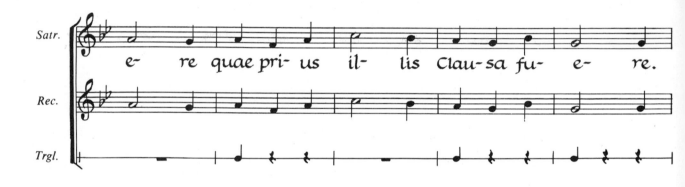

Then the King ascends his throne and Satraps acclaiming him say:

attacca

[19]

NARRATOR:

Mighty Belshazzar commands a feast;
A thousand lords give him thanks and glory.
Flushed and foolish, flown with pride,
He bids his servants to bring hither
The goodly goblets of gold and silver,
The consecrated cups and vessels
Set aside for sacred use
In Jehovah's temple, but taken thence
When Nebuchadnezzar annexed Judah.
His wanton wives drink wine therefrom.
With lustful lips and looks profane,
Their shouts grow shameless at Belshazzar's table
In honor of idols of their own devising
Forgetting God from whom all greatness comes.
In this heedless hour a hand appears,
Phantom fingers come forth and write
Words on the wall, a wonder to behold.

The sight silences; they cease laughing;
Full of fear is the face of the king,
Belshazzar of Babylon; his bowels quake,
His knees knock. In his need he cries:
"Summon my soothsayers, the sages of my
    kingdom
My wise men. Wealth shall he have,
Garments of scarlet and gold chains,
Who reads what is written, unriddles these
    words."
The loremasters, the learned of Babylon,
Are brought to the palace; they peer, they frown,
They stare astonished at the strange words;
They know them not; their knowledge is vain;
The truth is not in them to interpret rightly
What is said there. Sad at heart
Are the king and his court; care fills them.

Three boys exit to Palace entrance and return carrying a table and vessels (a seven-branched candelabrum, a chalice, and a bowl).

And the King speaks thus:

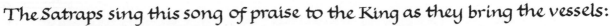

The men cross around the table, and drink with the King.

The Satraps sing this song of praise to the King as they bring the vessels:

[21]

Satr. Qui sic su- os per- or- na- vit pur-pu- ra et o- stro.

Trgl.

Prince I- ste_ po- tens, i- ste_ for- tis, i- ste glo- ri- o- sus,

Sm. Dr.

3 Men I- ste pro- bus, cu- ri- a- lis, de- cens et for- mo- sus.

Sm. Dr.

The Second Monk enters from upstage entrance, crosses all the way downstage, and writes on an imaginary wall until the Prince's solo is sung.

Prince Ju- bi- le- mus Re- gi tan- to vo- ci- bus ca- no- ris;

Trgl.
Sm. Cym.

Satr. Re- so- ne- mus o- mnes u- na lau- di- bus so- no- ris;

Men Re- so- ne- mus o- mnes u- na lau- di- bus so- no- ris;

Rec.
Oboe

Viola

Tamb.
Trgl.
Sm. Dr.
Sm. Cym.

Then the Princes say:

Prince Men
Ten., Bar.
Freely

Ec-ce sunt an-te fa - - ci - em ___ tu-am.

Meanwhile, a right hand appears before the King, writing on the wall:

MENE, TEKEL, PERES.

At the sound of the bells, all freeze.
The Second Monk walks in silence through the court and disappears in the upstage
area as Belshazzar begins.

Bell Carillon
f

The boys flee upstage left; the men try to flee upstage right. The Prince, ordered by
the King, stops the men. The King crosses to the handwriting.

The King, upon seeing it, is frightened and exclaims:

Belshazzar
In panic
f

Vo - ca-te ma-the- ma-ti- cos Chal-

Bells
f

Belsh.

dae-os, et a- ri- o- los. Au- ru-spi- ces in-

Bells

Belsh.

qui-ri- te, Et ma- gos in-tro-du- ci- te.

Bells

Then the wise men are brought, and they say to the King:

2 Wise Men
Timidly

Rex, in e- ter-num ___ vi- ve!

Trumpet

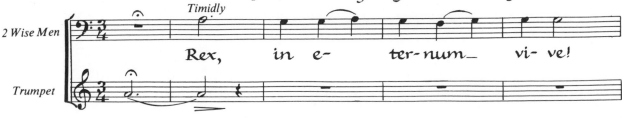

[26]

Ad- su- mus___ ec- ce ti- bi.

And the King says:

Belshazzar *With arrogance*

Qui scri- ptu-ram hanc le- ge- rit Et

sen- sum a- pe- ru- e- rit Sub il-

li- us po- ten- ti- a Sub- de- tur Ba- by-

lo- ni- a, Et in- si- gni-tus pur- pu-

ra Tor- que fru- e- tur au- re- a.

Not knowing how to solve the writing, they say to the King:

2 Wise Men *With fear*

1st

Ne- sci-mus per- sol- ve- re nec da- re con-

1st

si- li- um, Quae sit su- per scri- pti-

2nd

o, nec ma- nus in- di- ci- um.

The men cross slowly to the handwriting, make as if to touch it, and try to explain. Unable to do so, and disappointed, they cross upstage as the court sits in silence. The Narrator then begins.

[27]

NARRATOR:

News of this hap is noised abroad:
In her quiet quarters the Queen hears it,
And in loving haste leaves her chamber
To counsel the king. Comely her form,
Gracious to gaze on like the green cedar,
Blithe in bearing like a blossoming rose,
As she enters the hall with her handmaidens.
"My lord," she says, "Live for ever,
May thy days endure. There dwells in thy
   kingdom
A holy man, mighty in wisdom,
His speech inspired by the spirit of God,
Whom thy father favored for he found none
So apt to expound a hard sentence,
Unriddle visions and read the meaning

Of dark dreams. Daniel is his name.
Show him this writing, for surely he will
Interpret it truly. Be troubled no more!"
Hearkening to her counsel, the king says:
"Find me this man and fetch him hither!"
Searching the city, the satraps come
To Daniel's dwelling. "Come down," they call,
"And hasten with us to the High King,
He wishes for thy wisdom, great reward shall
   be thine
If thou canst tell him the true meaning
Of the secret signs, and assuage his fear."
"Princes," says the prophet, "if it please God,
The Lord of truth, to enlighten my spirit,
I will read these runes; direct me thither."

Four boys, the Queen, her attendant, and three more boys enter. The processional circles the acting area singing.

The processional of the Queen coming to the King:

ne- que sol- vit,___ quae sit___ ma-nus___ vi- si-   o.

Ec- ce___ pru-dens,___ styr-pe___ clu- ens,___ di- ves

cum po- ten- ti- a; In- ve- sti- tu

cresc. poco a poco

de- au- ra- to con- jux ad- est re- gi- a.

Haec la- ten-tem___ pro-met___ va- tem_ per cu-

jus___ in- di- ti- um Rex_ de- scri- bi

su~um i~bi____ no~ve~ rit. ex~ i~ti~ um.

Lae~tis___ er~go____ haec vi~ ra~ go___ co~mi~

[33]

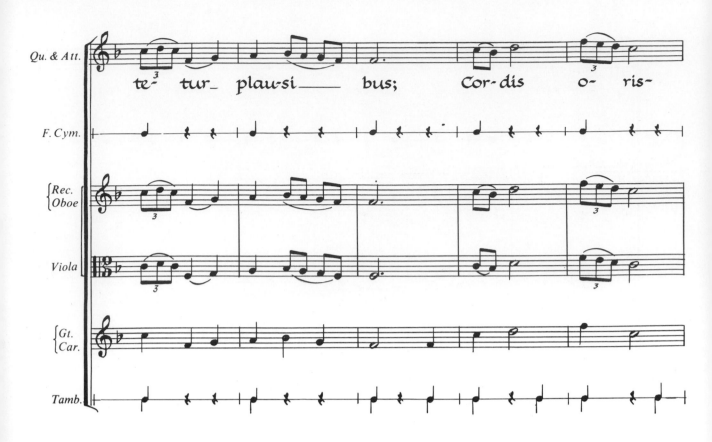

te- tur_ plau-si—— bus; Cor-dis o- ris-

que so- no-ris__ per-so- ne-tur vo-ci- bus.

Then the Queen comes before the King and venerates him, saying:

The King rises, and crosses to the handwriting.

The Queen crosses behind him, and points to the area from which Daniel will enter.

Upon hearing this, the King turns toward the Queen, and she continues:

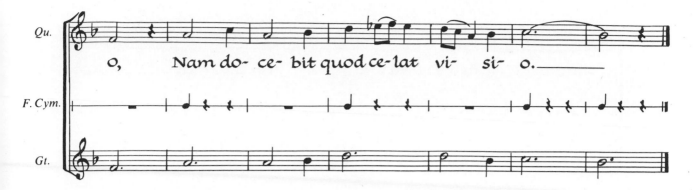

The King crosses back to the throne and sits. He orders the men to look for Daniel.

Then the King says to his princes:

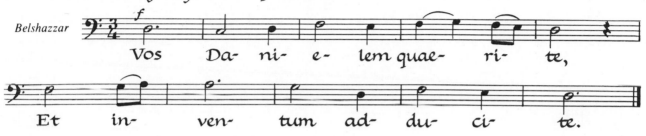

The men, singing, cross to Daniel's entrance. Daniel enters with zither player behind him.

Then the princes, having found Daniel, say to him:

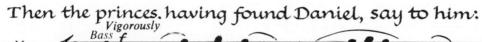

[1] V'yen ahl Roy (Old French).   [2] pahrlehr ah toy.

[37]

And Daniel answers them:

They walk to the acting area as they sing the following.

The processional of Daniel as he comes to the King:

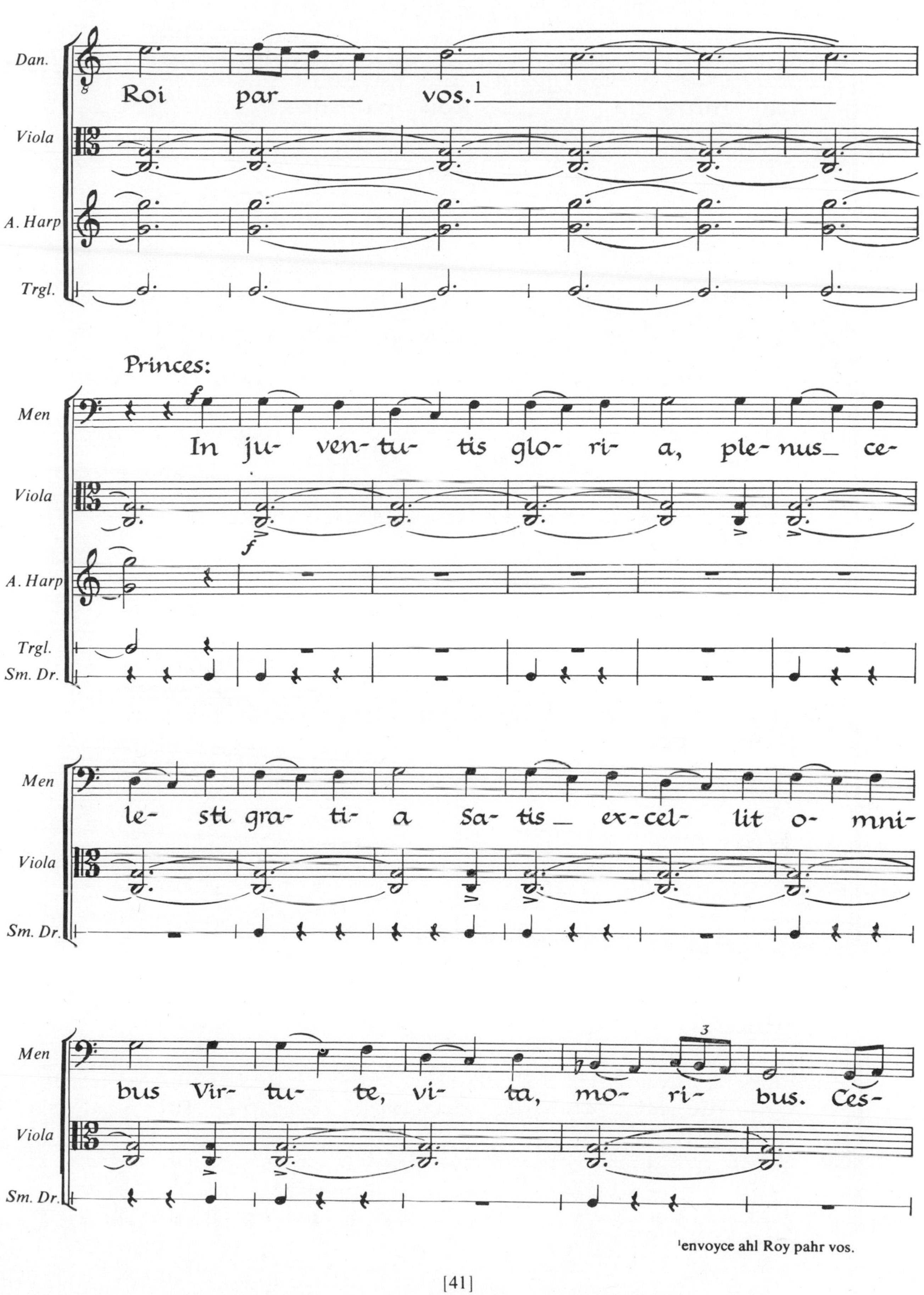

[1]envoyce ahl Roy pahr vos.

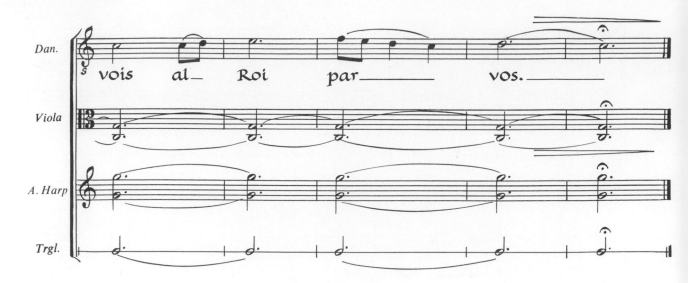

They all bow to the King, and the Narrator begins.

NARRATOR:

He is come to the court and the king says:
"Art thou that child of churlish Judah
Who is deemed wise? Is Daniel thy name?
My soothsayers, the sages of Babylon
Cannot understand the strange writing:
If thou canst make its meaning clear,
Glory and gold shall be given thee."
And Daniel answers: "Hail, O king!
When Nebuchadnezzar, as thou knowest well,
Forgot the God from whom his glory came
In the lust of his pride, the light of reason
Fled from him, he fed on grass
Like a brute beast. Thy boast is worse.
Thou has lifted thyself against the Lord of
    Heaven,
Profaning what was sacred, the vessels of His
    house,
Made obeisance to idols of brass and stone:

For this thou art judged. Thus I interpret
The words on the wall, a warning of doom.
MENE saith the Lord: thy might is finished.
TEKEL saith the Lord: tested in the balance,
Thou art found wanting, thy weight is less.
PERES saith the Lord: thy fall is certain,
Thy crown shall leave thee, thy kingdom be
    divided
Thy power apportioned to Persians and Medes."
Then Belshazzar is ashamed, he shakes with fear.
"I have sinned," he says, "Let the sacred vessels,
God's treasure, be returned to Judah
To own for ever. Let honor be shown
To this wise man in whose mouth is truth."
With merry music and mirthful song
The princes praise the prophet Daniel
The Queen also for her quickness of heart
And his lieges leave their lord alone.

Upon arriving before the King, Daniel says to him:

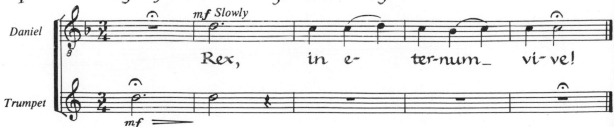

[44]

And the King answers Daniel:

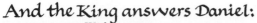

Belshazzar

With contempt

Tu-ne Da-ni- el no-mi-ne di-ce-ris,

Huc ad-du-ctus cum Ju-dae-ae mi-se-ris? Di-cunt te ha-

be-re De-i spi-ri-tum Et prae-sci-re quod-li-bet ab-

scon-di-tum. Si er-go po-tes scri-ptu-ram sol-ve-re,

Im-men-sis mu- ne-ri-bus di-ta-be-re.

Daniel crosses to the writing.   While singing, he crosses to the table, and handles the vessels.

And Daniel says to the King:

[47]

Daniel crosses to the handwriting.

segue

And the King replies:

All rise in silence, and two attendants ceremoniously drape the garment over Daniel's shoulders. Daniel sits next to the King, and all sit.

Daniel sits next to the King, adorned with royal garments. The King says to the prince of his troops:

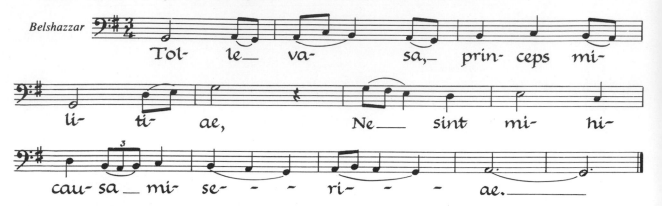

Then, after leaving the palace, the Satraps bring back the vessels. And the Queen leaves. Recessional of the Queen:

The Prince gives the candelabrum to Daniel. All except the King rise to sing the following, forming a procession which includes the instruments, table, and vessels. This procession goes through the audience, repeating the music until it is over. Here the cast changes costume and re-enters as Darius' Court.

Processional of those bringing the vessels before Daniel:

The King remains alone, and sits on his throne as the Narrator begins.

NARRATOR:

Now Belshazzar shivers as shades of night
Fall upon fields and fortified cities:
In solitude and silence his soul is delivered
To wanhope and weakness. "Ah, woe!," he sighs,
"My doom is upon me, death is near,
The fate foretold; what I fear will be.
Once God gave me glory and power,
Triumph for a time; now He takes them back;
Nor strength nor cunning can stay His hand.
The might of kings is in their many warriors,
Bowmen, spearmen and burnished chariots,
But His power is in Himself to impose His will;
He issues no orders, His heart intends
'Let this happen!' and, Lo! it does.
Men trust in towers, in turreted keeps
And high walls, but who can point

Upward or downward or out yonder,
This way or that, saying 'There He dwells'?
With a man one can bargain;—'Be my friend
And I will give you gold or cattle,
Horses or women,' but who can say
Of the Lord Almighty 'He lacks this.
I perceive the desire that will sway His judgment'?
Nor valor nor vanity avail me now.
I go to my grave, my glory is brought
To dust and darkness: but, as death takes me,
Let me turn to the Truth, entrust my soul
To the Lord of Light, the Living God!"
And now in the night there is noise of battle:
Darius the Great who rules the Medes,
Comes forth as a victor, invades the land,
Slays Belshazzar and sits on his throne.

Darius' procession enters from far entrance. They approach the King, who desperately
searches for an exit. Two Persian soldiers enter from upstage and kill Belshazzar.

[60]

Suddenly King Darius appears with his princes, and before him come the cyther players and his princes singing the following:

[65]

Before the King comes to his throne, two soldiers expel Belshazzar, rushing upon him as if to kill him.

Darius takes the throne.

Then, as King Darius sits in his majesty, the Court exclaims:

NARRATOR:

Now Darius rules: he raises Daniel
To high office for his excellent spirit,
Favors, befriends, prefers him over
Presidents and princes, plans to make him
Ruler of the realm. Wroth are the lords,
Jealous of this Jew. They join together,
Watch and wait for his ways to err,
But find no fault; he is faithful in all.
"We cannot," they say, "find occasion against him
Unless it relates to the Law of his God."

The Envious Counselors cross to opposite sides of the throne and conspire.

[68]

Then two men tell the King to have Daniel summoned, and the King orders him to be brought forth. Standing before the other princes, they sing the following:

Au-di- te, prin- ci- pes, re- ga- lis cu- ri- ae, Qui le- ges re- gi- tis_ to- ti- us pa- tri- ae.___ Est qui- dam sa- pi- ens in Ba- by- lo- ni- a, Se- cre- ta re- se- rans_ de- o- rum gra- ti- a.___ E- jus con- si- li- um re- gi com- pla- cu- it, Nam pri- us Bal- tha- sar scri- ptum a- pe- ru- it.___ I- te ve- lo- ci- ter, ne sit di- la- ti- o; Nos u- ti vo- lu- mus_ e- jus con- si- li- o.___ Fi- at si_ ve- ne- rit_ con- si- li- a- ri- us___ Re- gis,_ et fu- e- rit in_ re- gno ter- ti- us.___

Boys and men cross to the entrance of Daniel. He enters, the procession forms and they go to the King.

The legates, having found Daniel, say to him on the part of the King:

Er- go ve- ni, jam o- mnes_ cu- ri- a

Prae- pa- ra- tur ad tu- a_ gau- di- a.___

And Daniel replies:

Daniel

Slowly

Gen- vois al Roi._____

Autoharp (Zither)

The processional of Daniel:

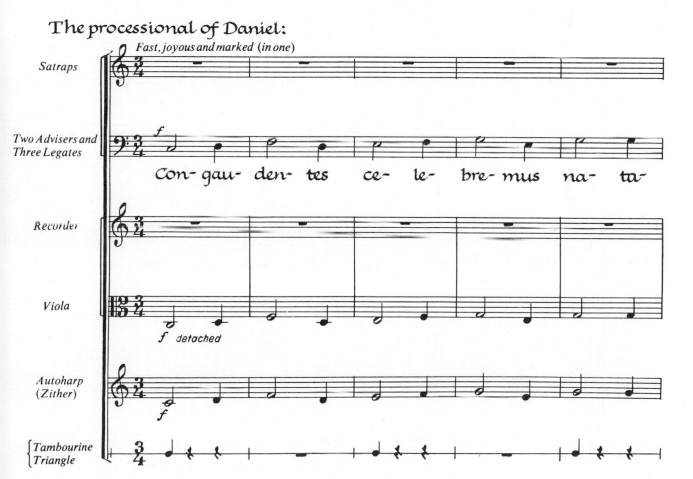

Satraps

Fast, joyous and marked (in one)

Two Advisers and Three Legates

Con- gau- den- tes ce- le- bre- mus na- ta-

Recorder

Viola

f detached

Autoharp (Zither)

Tambourine / Triangle

[72]

[73]

Leg. & Adv.: o- nis co- pi- a; Ces- sat re- gni

Viola

A. Harp

Tamb.

Leg. & Adv.: Ju- dae- o- rum con- tu- max po- ten- ti- a.

Viola

A. Harp

Tamb.

3 Men: *One* In hoc na- ta- li- ti- o, *Two* Da- ni- el, cum

Tamb.

3 Men: *Two* gau- di- o *Three* te lau- dat haec con- ti- o.

Tamb.

And Daniel says to the King:

The King addresses Daniel:

And Daniel replies to the King:

Then the King has him sit next to himself.

[78]

NARRATOR:

The plotting princes approach the king.
"Darius," they say, "may your reign be long!
The captains of your court have counselled
    together
To establish a statute, a stern decree.
This have we thought. For thirty days
Whosoever shall ask a petition
Of any save thee shall be thrown straightway
Alive to the lions. Long live Darius!
Wilt thou sign, great king, and seal the writing,
That none may annul this new law?"
Then Darius, thinking no evil,
Signs and seals it. The sinful men
Hurry hence to the house of Daniel
Where, at a window towards Jerusalem,
The prophet is praying with pure heart

To the true God. They return to Darius.
"O king," they cry, "thy decree went forth
That whosoever should ask a petition
Of any save thee should be thrown to the lions,
But this man Daniel has dared disobey thee;
Openly he asks for help from his God."
Darius is sad, he sees their envy;
He labors long to deliver Daniel.
But the accusers cry: "The decree was thine.
Didst thou not sign and seal the writing
That none should annul it? It shall not be changed."
"Alas," says the king, "the law is thus."
Grieving greatly, he gives orders
That Daniel be cast in the den of lions.
"Daniel," he cries, "I can do no other.
Forgive thy friend! May God save thee!"

The members of the Court leave upstage while the Envious Counselors step toward the throne.

And the other advisers, envious of Daniel because he finds more favor with the King, consult with the other princes on a plan to kill Daniel; they say to the King:

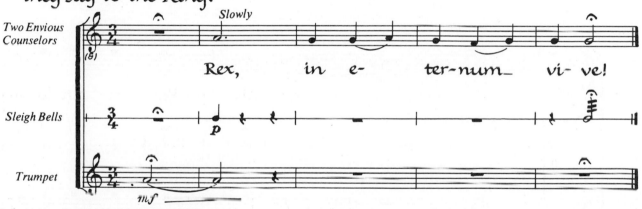

And they continue:

[79]

In le- o-num tra- da- tur fo- ve- am; Sic di- ca- tur per to- tam re- gi- am, O Rex!____

And the King says:

E- go man- do et re- man- do Ne sit

spre- tum hoc de- cre- tum. O- hez!

attacca

Daniel crosses downstage to pray, and kneels.

Daniel, on hearing this, retires to his house and adores his God. When those envious of him see this, they run to the King and say:

And the King, not knowing why they said this, answers:

[83]

Then they bring Daniel to the King and say to him:

Counts. Hunc Ju- dae-um su-um De-um Da- ni- e- lem vi- di- mus

A- do-ran-tem et pre-can-tem, tu- is spre-tis le- gi- bus.

The King, wishing to free Daniel, says:

Dar. Nun-quam vo-bis con-ce-da-tur___ Quod vir san-ctus sic per- da-tur.

The Satraps, on hearing this, show him the law and say:

Counts. Lex Par- tho-rum et Me-do-rum ju-bet in an- na- li- bus

Ut qui spre-vit quae de-cre-vit Rex, de- tur le- o- ni- bus.

The King, on hearing this, whether he will or no, says:

Darius stands.

Darius

Slowly and sadly

Si spre-vit le-gem quam sta-tu-e- ram Det
poe- nas i- pse quas de- cre- ve- ram.

Darius turns his back as he sends Daniel to the lions' den. The Envious Counselors seize Daniel.

Then the Satraps seize Daniel, and looking back toward the King, he says:

Daniel

Moderately slow, with intensity

He- u, he- u, he- u! Quo ca- su_ sor-
tis___ ve- nit haec_ da- mna-ti- o mor- tis? He- u,-
he- u, he- u! Sce- lus_ in- fan-dum! Cur me da-bit ad
la- ce- ran- dum Haec fe- ra tur- ba fe- ris? Sic
.me,_ Rex, per-de- re quae-ris? He- u! Qua
mor- te_ mo-ri me co- gis? Par- ce fu- ro- ri..

The King, unable to free him, says to him:

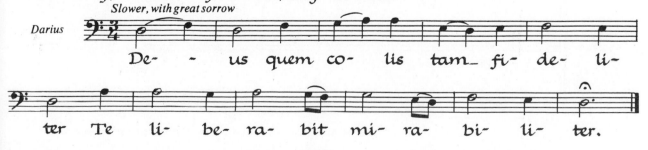

Darius

Slower, with great sorrow

De- - us quem co- lis tam_ fi- de- li-
ter Te li- be- ra- bit mi- ra- bi- li- ter.

[85]

Then they thrust Daniel into the pit.

The Envious Counselors throw Daniel to the lions as the Narrator begins.

NARRATOR:

So Daniel is down in the deep pit,
Alone among lions. But the Lord of Heaven
Sends an angel with a sword to keep
Those beasts at bay that they bite him not.
And a second angel He sends in the night
To Habakkuk, a holy prophet,
Saying: "Arise! The road is long.
I am bid to bring you to Babylon town
And the dark den where Daniel lies."
"That is full far," says that faithful man,
"And I know not the way; nevertheless
I will go to greet him." God's angel
Takes him by the hair; in a trice they come
To the perilous pit; he appears to Daniel,
Refreshes with food his fainting spirit.

Immediately an angel holding a sword keeps the lions at bay lest they touch him, and Daniel calls out as he goes into the pit:

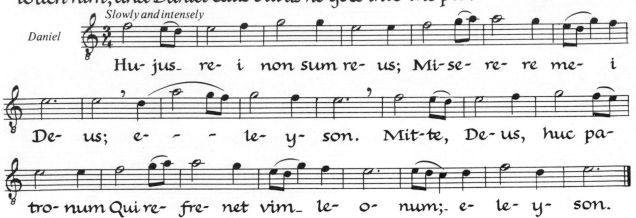

Slowly and intensely

Daniel: Hu- jus- re- i non sum re- us; Mi-se- re- re me- i De- us; e- - le- y- son. Mit-te, De- us, huc pa- tro- num Qui re- fre- net vim- le- o- num;- e- le- y- son.

The lions attack. An Angel appears with a sword and stops the lions. Habakkuk appears at the far entrance and walks quickly toward the stage area.

Meanwhile another angel brings a message to Habakkuk the prophet, to take the repast which he was bringing to his reapers to Daniel in the lions' den, saying:

The Angel* leads Habakkuk to the den of lions.

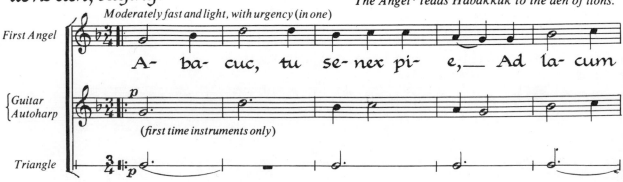

Moderately fast and light, with urgency (in one)

First Angel: A- ba- cuc, tu se- nex pi- e,— Ad la- cum

Guitar / Autoharp: *(first time instruments only)*

Triangle

*A second Angel may be used in this scene, depending on available forces.

Habakkuk answers him:

Da- ni- el est po- si- tus.

attacca

Then the angel, taking him by the hair of his head, leads him to the den, and Habakkuk says to Daniel as he offers him the repast:

Sur- ge,— fra-ter, ut ci- bum ca- pi- as; Tu-

as— De-us vi- dit an- gu- sti- as; De- us—

mi-sit, da De- o gra- ti- as, Qui te— fe- cit.

Daniel, taking the food, says:

When this has been done, the Angel takes Habakkuk back to his place.

Darius rises and moves toward the den. The Narrator begins.

NARRATOR:

Day dawns; to the den of lions
The king is come. He calls aloud:
"Daniel, O Daniel, my dear friend,
Dost thou live yet? Hath the Lord thy God
Saved his servant from sudden death?"
And Daniel answers: "Hail, O king!
I am safe and sound. God sent an angel
With a shining sword to shut the mouths
Of the hungry lions. They lie asleep."
Glad is Darius at this great wonder,
Bids his bodyguard bring up Daniel,
Set him free, and in fury commands:
"Let his accusers be cast in the pit!"

The princes and presidents who plotted evil
Rue their wrong. Ere they reach the bottom
Their bones are broken, their bodies rent,
Torn in pieces by the teeth of the lions.
So Daniel was restored to his state of honor
And dwelt in peace until his days end.
Visions revealed to him events to come;
Truly he foretold the return of Judah
To its own home, and the end of Jerusalem,
Her final fall when, in fullness of time,
The wise Word that was from the beginning,
Maker of all things, should be made flesh
And suffer death to redeem mankind.

Then the King descends from his throne, comes to the den, and says in tears:

[89]

ri- pi- a- ris A ne- ce pro- po- si-

ta,— quem tu co- lis et ve- ne- ra- ris?

Darius recognizes Daniel. The trumpet sound brings the entire court in.

And Daniel says to the King: He

Daniel

Fast and joyously

Rex, in e- ter-num vi- ve!— An-

Trumpet

continues:

ge- li- cum so- li- ta mi- sit pi- e- ta- te pa- tro- num,—

Quo De- us ad tem- pus con- pe- scu- it o- ra le- o- - num.

Then the King rejoicing says:

Darius

Somewhat slower, with strength

Da- ni-

Trumpet

Small Cymbals

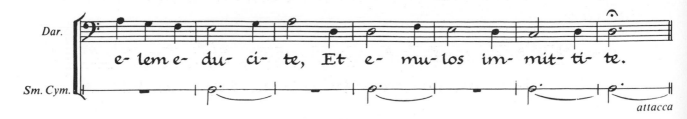

Dar.

e- lem e- du- ci- te, Et e- mu- los im- mit- ti- te.

Sm. Cym.

attacca

[90]

When those have been stripped of their robes and brought before the pit, they exclaim:

The men throw the Envious Counselors to the lions and the Court cries out.

When they have been thrown into the pit, they are immediately consumed by the lions; and when the King sees this he says:

Daniel and Darius cross to the throne area.

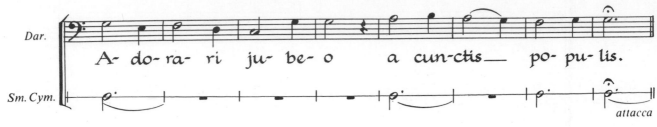

Moderately

Darius: De-um Da-ni-e- lis qui re-gnat in sae-cu-lis

Small Cymbals

Dar.: A-do-ra-ri ju-be-o a cun-ctis— po-pu-lis.

Sm. Cym.

attacca

Same Tempo

Satraps: De-um Da-ni-e- lis qui re-gnat in sae-cu-lis

Soldiers: De-um Da-ni-e- lis qui re-gnat in sae-cu-lis

Recorder / Oboe

Viola

Guitar / Autoharp

All Percussion

[92]

All kneel in front of Darius and Daniel. Daniel motions the Court to rise as he sings.

When Daniel has been received into his former place of glory, he prophesies:

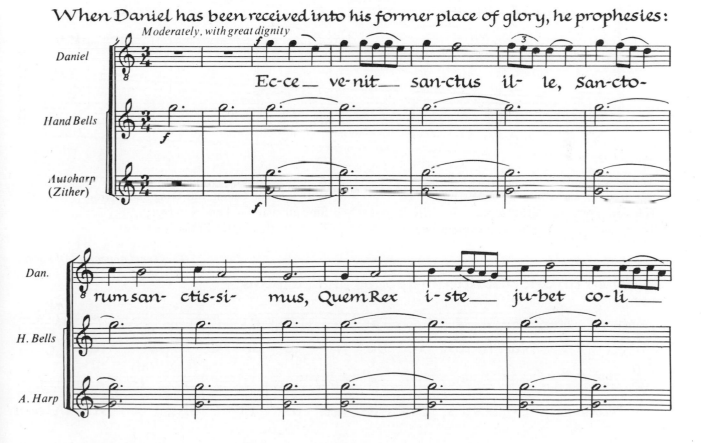

NARRATOR:

And now, good people, our play is done.
But, to grace our going, let God's angel
Tell you tidings of eternal joy.
To the maiden Mary, the immaculate Virgin,

A baby is born in Bethlehem City.
Who is called Christ, our King and Saviour.
Sing glory to God and goodwill,
Peace to all people! Praise the Lord!

The Angel appears. All kneel.

Then an angel suddenly appears and exclaims:

[94]

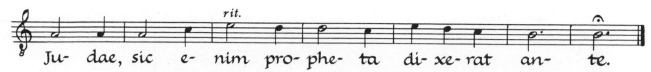

Ju- dae, sic e- nim pro- phe- ta di- xe- rat an- te.

During the "Te Deum" all rise slowly, form a procession, and exit through the audi-
ence. As music fades the Angel turns slowly and walks upstage. At the end nothing is
heard but the bells slowly fading out.

After hearing this the cantors intone the "Te Deum Laudamus":

[95]

Finit Daniel

Bell Carillon continues after Te Deum, fading out slowly

GUIDE TO LATIN Pronunciation

The most practical solution to the problem of pronunciation in the modern performance of *The Play of Daniel* is to use church Latin of the contemporary Roman usage, as it is most widely accepted today. The following listing of vowels and consonants will serve as a guide. In other diphthongs and groups of consonants the letters are pronounced separately.

a	as in father	p*a*ter
e	as in met	*e*cce
i	as in police	Chr*i*ste
o	as in for	*o*mnes
u	as in who (oo)	j*u*bilem*u*s
y	as "i" above	Bab*y*lon
ae oe	as in met	Jude*ae*
c	(before e,ae,oe,i,y) as *ch* in church	*c*essant
c	(except as above) as in car	vo*c*ate
ch	as in character	*Ch*riste
g	(before e,ae,oe,i,y) as in generous	re*g*is
g	(except as above) as in government	er*g*o
gn	as in onion (nyuh)	ma*gn*a
h	not pronounced (except mihi—miki)	*h*onorem
j	as in yes (Latin "y" or "i")	*J*erusalem
s	as in sea	*s*ed
sc	(before e,ae,oe,i,y) as *sh* in shed	ne*sc*imus
ti	(before a vowel and following any letter except s,x,t) as in Be*tsy*	gra*ti*a
th	as in Thomas (t)	ma*th*ematicos
x	as in maxim (ks)	re*x*
xc	(before e,ae,oe,i,y) as in bookshelf	e*xc*elsis

THE PLAY OF DANIEL Translation OF THE LATIN TEXT

BY JEAN MISRAHI

In your honor, Christ,
This Daniel Play
Was written at Beauvais,
The product of our youth.

*As King Belshazzar approaches, his princes sing
this song before him:*

To the almighty holder of the firmament
This throng of men and boys
    Assembled gives praise.

For it listens attentively
To the many things faithful Daniel
    Underwent and suffered.

The King calls before him the wise men
To explain the meaning of the letters
    Written by that hand.

Since the wise men were not able to solve them,
Silent before the King
    They held their tongues.

But to Daniel, upon reading the writing,
It became clear at once
    What had been hidden to them.

When Belshazzar saw how he excelled the others
He placed him above them in the hall,
    So it is related.

A case, not very solid, found against him,
And sentenced him to be torn
    By the teeth of the lions.

But, O God, it was then your wish
That those who had been cruel to Daniel
    Should become kind.

And to him, lest he fall faint,
You sent bread by the angel-borne prophet,
    Bringing him food.

BELSHAZZAR'S FEAST

*Then the King ascends his throne and Satraps ac-
claiming him say:*

Long live the King!

And the King speaks thus:

You who obey my voice,
Bring those vessels for my use
Which my father brought from the temple
When he severely crushed Judaea.

*The Satraps sing this song of praise to the King
as they bring the vessels:*

Let us praise our King,
 great and powerful!
Let us resound with worthy praise
 and fitting song!
Let the merry throng break forth
 in solemn chants;
Let them play their harps, clap their hands,
 sing a thousand tunes.
His father did a great thing in destroying
 the temple of the Jews,
And now this one reigns
 by his father's example.
His father took great booty
 from the kingdom of the Jews;
Now this one can make his feasts more splendid
 with such handsome vessels.
These are the royal vessels
 which were taken
From Jerusalem, and now adorn
 regal Babylon.
Let us present them to Belshazzar,
 to our King
Who vests his subjects
 in costly purple.
He is powerful, he is strong;
 he is glorious.
He is valiant, courtly,
 handsome and comely.
Let us praise so great a King
 in sonorous voices;
Together let us sound forth
 in harmonious praises.
With laughter, Babylon rejoices;
 Jerusalem weeps.
She has been deprived of her children, while
 Babylon in triumph venerates King
  Belshazzar.

Therefore, let everyone rejoice
 at such great power,
Offering these vessels of the king
 to His Majesty.

Then the princes say:

Behold, they are here before you.

*Meanwhile, a right hand appears before the King,
writing on the wall the following:* MENE, TEKEL,
PERES. *The King, upon seeing it, is frightened
and exclaims:*

Call forth the Chaldaean astrologers
And the diviners;
Search out the soothsayers,
And bring forth the wise men.

*Then the wise men are brought, and they say to
the King:*

Long live the King!
Behold, we are here before you.

And the King says:

Whoever reads this writing
And unfolds its meaning
Shall be given power
Over Babylon,
And arrayed in purple
Shall wear a golden collar.

*Not knowing how to solve the writing, they say to
the King:*

We cannot solve the writing
 nor give a clue
As to what is written
 nor find the meaning of the hand.

*The processional of the Queen coming to the
King:*

All the learned and the wise are now
 present in assembly,
Turning over in their minds, but unable to explain
 the vision of the hand.
Behold the royal spouse, the prudent,
 rich in power,

[104]

Adorned in golden garments,
    noble in her race.
She will bring forth the unknown prophet
    through whose interpretation
The King will learn and be told
    of his destruction.
Accompanied by joyful acclamations
    she then comes forward;
With sonorous tones of strings and voices
    let music now be made.

*Then the Queen comes before the King and vener-
ates him saying:*

Long live the King!
That you may know the meaning of the writing,
King Belshazzar, listen to this counsel.

*Upon hearing this, the King turns toward the
Queen, and she continues:*

Together with the captives of Judaea
One Daniel, learned in prophetic oracles,
Was brought to here, far from his home,
Captured by your father's victory.

Since he lives now under your rule,
Reason demands he be summoned here.
Command at once, let there be no delay,
For he will explain what the vision conceals.

Then the King says to his princes:

Go you to seek out Daniel,
Find him and bring him here.

*Then the princes, having found Daniel, say to
him:*

O prophet of God, Daniel,
    come to the King.
Come, he wishes
    to speak with you.
He is afraid and disturbed, Daniel,
    come to the King.
He wishes to know from you
    what is hidden from us.
He will enrich you with gifts, Daniel,
    come to the King.
If he can learn through you
    the meaning of the writing.

And Daniel answers them:

I am much in wonder on whose advice
The royal command seeks me out.
I shall go, nonetheless, and make known,
Unrewarded, what is hidden.

*The processional of Daniel as he comes to the
King:*

This true servant of God
Whom every people praises,
The fame of whose wisdom
Is known to the court of the King,
He is called to the King by us.

Daniel:

In poverty and in exile
I go to the King with you.

Princes:

In the glory of his youth,
Full of heavenly graces,
He completely excels all others
In virtue, life, and character.
He is called to the King by us.

Daniel:

In poverty and in exile
I go to the King with you.

Princes:

This is he whose help
Will solve that vision,
Which by the writing hand
Deeply moved the King.
He is called to the King by us.

Daniel:

In poverty and in exile
I go to the King with you.

*Upon arriving before the King, Daniel says to
him:*

Long live the King!

DANIEL REPROVES BELSHAZZAR

And the King answers Daniel:

Are you not called Daniel,
Brought here with the wretches of Judaea?
They say you have the spirit of God
And foresee whatever is hidden.
If then you can solve this writing,
You will be enriched with countless gifts.

And Daniel says to the King:

O King, I wish not your gifts;
Unrewarded I will solve the letters.
This is the solution:
Affliction awaits you.
Your father above all others
Once was powerful.
Swollen with excessive pride
He was cast down from glory.

For, not walking with God,
But making of himself a god,
He stole the vessels of the temple
And put them to his own use.
But after many such mad deeds
At the end he lost his wealth,
And deprived of human form,
He fed on repasts of grass.

And you, his son, as well,
No less wicked than he,

In following his example,
Use these very same vessels.
Since this is displeasing to God,
The time of His vengeance is at hand,
For the meaning of the writing
Is to warn of retribution.

For MENE, says the Lord,
Is the end of your kingdom;
TEKEL means a measuring weight,
Which means you are weaker;
PERES, that is division,
Your kingdom will be given to another.

And the King replies:

Let him who has solved the secret
Be adorned with regal robes.

Daniel sits next to the King, adorned with royal garments. The King says to the prince of his troops:

Take away the vessels, prince of my troops,
Lest they be the cause of misfortune to me.

Then, after leaving the palace, the Satraps bring back the vessels. And the Queen leaves.

Recessional of the Queen:

In the Book of Solomon is written
Fitting and becoming praise to women.

Her price is that of a valiant one
From the far and remotest corners of the earth.

Her husband's heart relies on her
Though he be rich in material wealth.

Let his woman be compared to the one
Who is a support to her king.

For her power of speech
Defeats the wisdom of the learned.

We who have this solemn day
Occasion to perform this play,

With reverence sing her praise
Let all come along and join in song.

*Processional of those bringing the vessels before
Daniel:*

Bringing back the vessels of that King
Whom the Jewish people fear,
Giving praise to Daniel,
    Let us rejoice!
Fitting praise to him
    Let us offer!

He foresaw the downfall of the King
When he solved the writing;
He proved the witnesses false,
And freed Susanna.
    Let us rejoice!
Fitting praise to him
    Let us offer!

Babylon exiled him
When she captured the Jews,
Belshazzar honored him.
    Let us rejoice!
Fitting praise to him
    Let us offer!

He is a holy prophet of God,
Even the Chaldaeans honor him,
Together with the Gentiles and the Jews,
Therefore in acclaiming him,
    Let us rejoice!
Fitting praise to him
    Let us offer!

*Suddenly King Darius appears with his princes,
and before him come the string players and his
princes singing the following:*

Behold King Darius
Approaching with his princes,
The noble with his nobles.

And his entire court
Resounds with joyousness,
And dances are there too.

He is admired,
Venerated by all.
There are many kingdoms
Subject to him.

All honor the King
And adore him.

Him Babylon fears
And his fatherland.

Assaulting with his troops
And with his weapons
He destroys enemy hosts,
And crushes even the strong.
Honor and nobility
Adorn him.

Here is King Darius,
The noble Babylonian.
Let the throng in dance
Rejoice with him.
Let them praise with great joy
His powerful deeds,
The wonder of all.

Let us all give thanks together;
Let the drums sound forth;
Let the harp players pluck their strings;
Let the instruments of the musicians
Resound in his praise.

*Before the King comes to his throne two soldiers
expel Belshazzar, rushing upon him as if to kill
him. Then, as King Darius sits in his majesty,
the Court exclaims:*

Long live the King!

THE MURDER OF BELSHAZZAR

*Then two men tell the King to have Daniel sum-
moned, and the King orders him to be brought
forth. Standing before the other princes, they
sing the following:*

Listen, O princes of the royal court,
Who make the laws of the whole land.

There is one most wise in Babylonia,
Who by the grace of God opens all secrets.

His counsel pleased the King,
For he revealed the meaning of the writing to Belshazzar.

Go quickly, let there be no delay;
We wish to employ his counsel.

If we will come, let him be counselor
To the King, and be third in the kingdom.

*The Legates, having found Daniel, say to him on
the part of the King:*

Our legation, O servant of God,
Comes from the royal command.

Your worth has been praised to the King,
Your great judgment commends you.

Through you alone was made clear to us
That writing of the hand, obscure to all.

The King calls you to his court
That he may know your wisdom.

You shall be, so said Darius,
The first of his advisers.

Come then, for the whole court
Is preparing to greet you with joy.

And Daniel replies:

I go to the King.

The processional of Daniel:

Rejoicing, let us celebrate
    the solemnity of Christmas;
For we are redeemed from death
    by the Wisdom of God.

He is born as man in the flesh,
    who created all,
Whose birth was foretold
    by the words of the prophet.

Now has ceased the old anointing,
    as Daniel did foretell;
And now ceases the stubborn power
    of the kingdom of the Jews.

On this Christmas feast,
    Daniel, with joy
        this throng praises you.

From that deadly accusation
    you redeemed Susanna
When His holy inspiration
    God breathed into you.

You proved the accusers false,
    guilty of their accusation;
You overcame the dragon, Bel,
    before the throng of the people.

And God watched over you
    in the lions' den.
Praise be then to the Word of God
    of a Virgin born.

And Daniel says to the King;

Long live the King!

The King addresses Daniel:

Because I know you are sagacious,
The guardian of all this realm,
O Daniel, I appoint you,
And set you in the highest place.

And Daniel replies to the King:

O King, if you place your trust in me,
Through my fault you will do no wrong.

*Then the King has him sit next to himself. And
the other advisers, envious of Daniel because
he finds more favor with the King, consult with
the other princes on a plan to kill Daniel; they
say to the King:*

Long live the King!

And they continue:

It was decreed in your court
By those who rule in glory
That by the authority of your name
All other gods should be ignored
For the space of thirty days
And you be adored as the god of all,
     O King!

If anyone be rash in boldness
And be opposed to your command,
Adore another god than you,
So firm let then the judgment be
That he be thrown in the lions' den;
Let this be cried through all the realm,
     O King!

And the King says:

I demand and command
That this decree respected be
     Here ye!

Daniel, on hearing this, retires to his house and adores his God. When those envious of him see this, they run to the King and say:

Darius, did you not decree
     this should be obeyed by all,
That none adore nor yet implore
     any god but you alone,

DANIEL PRAYING IN HIS HOME

The man who disobeys this law
     to the lions should be thrown;
This was ordained and so proclaimed
     by the princes of the land.

And the King, not knowing why they said this, answers:

I truly command to every man
That I be adored throughout the land.

Then they bring Daniel to the King and say to him:

Daniel the man of Judaea
     we saw worshiping his God,
Him adoring and imploring
     in defiance of your laws.

The King, wishing to free Daniel, says:

It will never be granted to you
That this holy man should perish so.

The Satraps, on hearing this, show him the law and say:

The law of the Parths and the Medes
     in the annals does command
That he who does not heed the King's decree
     to the lions should be thrown.

The King, on hearing this, whether he will or no, says:

If he disdained the law proclaimed
Let him be punished as ordained.

Then the Satraps seize Daniel, and looking back toward the King he says:

Alas, Alas, Alas!
By what fate am I condemned to death?
Alas, Alas, Alas!
O unspeakable crime!
Why does this crowd of cruel men
Give me to be torn in the wild beasts' den?
Is it thus, O King, that you wish me to perish?
Alas!
By what death do you doom me to die?
Spare your anger.

DANIEL IS CAST INTO THE DEN

The King, unable to free him, says to him:

The God you worship so faithfully
Will liberate you miraculously.

Then they thrust Daniel into the pit. Immediately an angel holding a sword keeps the lions at bay lest they touch him, and Daniel calls out as he goes into the pit:

For this charge I am not guilty;
Have mercy on me, O God;
      eleison.
Send, O God, a protector here
To restrain the lions' power;
      eleison.

Meanwhile another angel brings a message to Habakkuk the prophet, to take the repast which he was bringing to his reapers to Daniel in the lions' den, saying:

Habakkuk, O holy old man,
Take the meal to Daniel
In the den at Babylon;
The King of all commands you.

Habakkuk answers him:

The omniscience of God knows well
That I know not Babylon,
Nor is the den known to me
In which Daniel has been placed.

Then the angel, taking him by the hair of his head, leads him to the den, and Habakkuk says to Daniel as he offers him the repast:

Rise up, brother, and take the food:
God has seen your afflictions;
God has sent it, give thanks to God,
      The God who made you.

And Daniel, taking the food, says:

O Lord, You have remembered me.
This food in Your name I accept.
      Alleluia!

When this has been done, the Angel takes Habakkuk back to his place. Then the King descends from his throne, comes to the den, and says in tears:

Think you, Daniel, that you will be
      saved and snatched away
From this intended death by the One
      you worship and venerate?

And Daniel says to the King:

Long live the King!

He continues:

An angelic protector He has sent
      in His customary mercy
By whom God constrained in time
      the mouths of the lions.

Then the King rejoicing says:

Bring Daniel out,
Throw the envious in.

When these have been stripped of their robes and brought before the pit, they exclaim:

We suffer justly for we have sinned
      against this holy man of God,
We have acted wickedly,
      we have done iniquity.

When they have been thrown into the pit they are immediately consumed by the lions, and when the King sees this he says:

I command that the God of Daniel
Who reigns forever be adored by all.

When Daniel has been received into his former place of glory, he prophesies:

Behold, the holy one comes,
          the most holy of the holy,
Whom the King, mighty and powerful,
          commands you to adore.

The temples cease, the kingdom ends,
          the anointings also shall be over;
The end of the kingdom of the Jews
          and its suppression is at hand.

Then an angel suddenly appears and exclaims:

I bring you a message from on high:
Christ is born, the Ruler of the word,
In Bethlehem of Judaea, just as the prophet
          has foretold.

After hearing this, the cantors intone the "Te Deum Laudamus."

THE END OF THE PLAY OF DANIEL

THE VISION OF DANIEL

[111]

NOTES ON *Staging* THE PLAY

BY NIKOS PSACHAROPOULOS

The director of *The Play of Daniel* is immediately confronted with some unique problems which are created by the nature of the play itself and go beyond his basic task of staging it. The play was originally conceived, of course, for performance in a cathedral or church, and the ideal setting for a contemporary production—with the various exits and entrances for the players, the aisles for processions, and the chancel as the staging area for the drama—is still the church. The auditorium, as such, did not exist at the time the play was written, but a modern auditorium can make a fine setting for *The Play of Daniel*. (It must be noted that, for presentation in an auditorium, one structural addition is necessary: there must be steps leading to the stage from three points, for reasons which will be outlined below. In most auditoriums this will involve the addition of steps leading up to the front center of the stage.) In either setting, the success of the performance will be determined by the degree of careful preparation of the drama, music, scenery, costuming, and narration, as well as by proper organization of the available architectural factors of stage, exits, and aisles.

Aside from its liturgical aspects, *The Play of Daniel* is basically a thirteenth-century opera with a large number of processionals and recessionals; the singer-actors enter from, exit to, and perform in definitely specified areas. The problem of the physical location of the entrances and exits is of great importance in staging the play, as they carry with them the implications of the space surrounding the stage area. Thus, for example, in our performances we indicated the great outside world by a distant entrance at the rear of the nave. This served for the entrance of the musicians at the beginning of the play, for the approach of the attacking Persian army, and for the final exit. We used a side entrance, connoting the immediate outside world, for the entrances of Daniel, Habakkuk, and the Narrator. The third entrance was an easily accessible one through which the King and Queen moved, by implication, to other parts of the palace.

The choice of these entrance-exits and of the passageways from them to the stage is determined primarily by two factors: the duration of the processionals, and the ground-plan of the area being used. The stage is organized in terms of these areas of activity. The King's throne is raised on a platform at stage right toward the rear, with the lesser thrones, for the Queen and Daniel, on his left and right. The center of the stage will then be occupied by the courtiers and Daniel, and the left side by the musicians. The lions' den should be raised, and as far to the rear as practicable; and a pulpit, or lectern, for the Narrator should be at stage left front, so situated that he can seem to be an objective onlooker to the proceedings as well as a commentator. The problem posed for modern audiences by the Latin text is

THE CITY OF BABYLON

actually a minor one: Auden's narrative is sufficient to provide a clear exposition of the action.
In addition, the Narrator has a further unifying
function: his rendering of the narrative should
create the world of the play, dramatize the inci-
dents, and build the suspense. He should combine
the authority and grandeur of a high ecclesiastical
figure with all the excitement of a ringmaster. The
timing of his narration is crucial; for example, the
Queen's processional should start *before* the Narrator's last line, and the sound of the battle drum
should underline his description of the attack.

The Cloisters production made much use of
emphatic movement and gesture to convey details
of character and emotion; humility was expressed
by Daniel's bowed head; arrogance by Belshazzar's bearing. The two lions assumed an heraldic
pose after their entrance, giving an underlying
sense of playfulness to their clawing and threaten-
ing. Dumb show can most effectively be used in
certain scenes when the action is to continue without music or speech: immediately after the handwriting appears on the wall, when the entire court
freezes and the Second Monk walks silently and

sternly upstage through the court, giving a def-
inite premonition of catastrophe; when Belshazzar, crushed by the prophecies, orders his attendants to adorn Daniel. Another important factor
to be considered is the power of strong pictorial
dramatization: the Court, drinking and reveling
around its monarch; the bowed heads of the con-
spirators; the subdued lions being caressed by
Daniel; the advance of the Persian army, with its
warrior-king following, holding his sword before
him like a banner. In the first production of the
play the handwriting on the wall appeared upstage, making the cast turn toward it and away
from the audience. In the second production we
felt that if the writing was placed between the
audience and the performers, the latter would
then be able to wheel toward the audience and
create a more compelling effect. At the last, the
Archangel should appear—giving the impression
of almost floating in—in the most prominent, perhaps highest part of the stage rear, where he
should stand silently before singing; all should
bow down to him.

What degree of pictorial and archaeological ac-
curacy should the director strive for in producing
the play? Certainly the text and the original stage
directions should be followed with great care;
they are quite specific on certain points, and
greatly aid our view of the play in the light of its
time. In addition, medieval illumination and
sculpture can be both a guide to the director and
an inspiration in the staging. The scenes of the
killing of the King, the gestures of the Court, the
carrying of the Queen's train, among others,
would greatly profit by a resemblance to similar
scenes to be found in medieval art. The vast vo-
cabulary of symbolic usages of the Middle Ages
may well also be drawn upon in preparing the
production. On the other hand, it would be an er-
ror to become so involved in a mere imitation of
the twelfth and thirteenth centuries as to lose
sight of the Biblical story and its Christian message. This story and this message were the funda-
mental sources of inspiration to the author and to
the Beauvais cast, and they should remain so for
us. A production of *The Play of Daniel* which
captures the excitement and passion of the ancient
tale, and presents it with unpretentious clarity and
full respect for its integrity, will best show the
play as the great work of art that it is.

Narrator
& 2nd Monk

2nd Angel

Attendant
to Daniel

DANIEL

1st Angel

Lions

NOTES ON THE # Costumes BY ROBERT FLETCHER

When costuming *The Play of Daniel*, remember that for the most part the people of the Middle Ages represented the inhabitants of such scenes in contemporary clothes, or in a fancy-dress version of the same, not in what we have come to know as "Biblical dress." You will have a much more satisfactory and unusual production if you try to do the same. Go to early illuminations and cathedral sculpture for inspiration. Your Kings and Queens should look like those on the west front of Chartres Cathedral, not like the carvings at Nakshi Rustam and Khorsabad. Your soldiers are Norman knights, not ancient Persian bowmen.

Choose a separate color scheme for each of the two courts; for instance, you might use the brilliant blues and greens of Romanesque enamels for the Babylonians, and earth reds and browns with purple for the Persians.

Dress Daniel in white and his attendant zither player in shadowy gray or pale blue. The rich raiment that is given to him should be a long stole of heavy golden cloth ornamented with braid and fringe, and lined with bright purple or brilliant red. Do not make the lions too realistic. Most early medieval representations of such beasts are obviously not drawn from nature. They have a kind of gentle ferocity—something between a St. Bernard and an enlarged kitten. The monks should wear white gowns with black scapulars and hoods. Rose, orange, and gold are good colors for the angels. Their wings need not be all white. Many medieval pictures give them peacock and butterfly hues.

If you make the costumes yourself, choose unpatterned fabrics—soft woolens, linens, and rough woven silks, or, of course, cheaper substitutes that resemble them. Remember that people of this time would not have used faceted stones. The jewels in the crowns and on the clothing should all be cabochon cut. If you cannot get them, rock candy, bits of plastic, pebbles, mosaics, and buttons will all serve.

If you do not have a choir large enough to supply two separate groups of singers remember that the satraps, musicians, legates, and advisers of Belshazzar's court must change costume very quickly to become the soldiers, counselors, and advisers of the Persian court. The children and the man who plays Belshazzar's Prince, the chief envious counselor, and the second angel must all have three changes apiece.

The accompanying drawings are taken from the New York Pro Musica production and may be of some help to those who undertake to stage *The Play of Daniel*.

Babylonian Court

Herald

Musicians and men of the Court
& Legates

Satraps
(children)

BELSHAZZAR

CHANGE TO

Queen & Attendants

Belshazzar's
Prince

Wise men,
Advisers

Persian Court

Habakkuk

Envious
Counselors

DARIUS

Chief Envious Counselor

Persian Soldiers

CREDITS

The format for *The Play of Daniel* was designed by John Begg; the music autographed by Carl A. Rosenthal; calligraphy by Riki Levinson; illustrations of his own costume designs by Robert Fletcher. Copy for the medieval illustrations was furnished by the Pierpont Morgan Library. The text was photo-composed by The Science Press, Inc., on the Photon, printed by the Murray Printing Company and bound by Sendor Bindery, Inc.